Key Facts

Jupiter School is very old and lots of strange things happen there.

Cassie finds the magic book in the library. When she opens it, the things inside come to life.

Iron

Fairies do not like iron. It can burn them or make them feel sick.

Story Background

Cassie is being bullied at her new school. She hides in the library and finds a strange book. When the Fairy Queen escapes, Cassie has a big problem...

Jupiter School is very old. Lots of odd things happen there.

Cassie is new. Some of the girls are mean to her.

Jinx

BY **CHLOE LEWIS**

ILLUSTRATED BY **SARA FORESTI**

Walkthrough

Read this first - or turn the page to go straight to the story!

The Characters

Cassie

Cassie is the new girl at school. She wants to fit in but the bullies won't leave her alone!

Tiff

Tiff is Cassie's friend. She comes from a family of witches. She knows a lot about magic.

The Fairy Queen

The Fairy Queen escapes the magic book. Can Cassie and Tiff get her back before she causes too much havoc?

Cassie likes the library. No one goes in there and she can be alone. One day, Cassie sees a strange book.

Please open...

The clasp lifts with a click. The book is full of magical beasts. Cassie sees a picture of a fairy queen.

The bullies come into the library. They are looking for Cassie. One bully takes the book.

There is a flash and the fairy queen flies out of the book. She casts a curse on the bullies and they turn into rats.

Tiff jumps out from behind a shelf.

The fairy queen screeches.

The fairy queen flies off.

How did you know that?

Tiff explains that she is from a family of witches.

She knows about magic like this.

Cassie looks at the rats on the floor. She feels bad.

I bet you're really scared.
I'm sorry.

Cassie puts the book and the rats in her bag to keep them safe. Cassie and Tiff look all over the school. Suddenly...

Cassie sees her chance. Cassie sneaks up
behind the fairy queen with the book.

Cassie shuts the book around the fairy queen.
There is a flash as the clasp shuts.

Join the Court...

Answer the questions below. Each correct answer gains you points. Are you a Troll or a Fairy Queen?

1 *Multiple Choice:*
What do the bullies do to Cassie's bag? **1pt**
a) They throw it in the mud
b) They steal it
c) They throw it over a fence

2 *Multiple Choice:*
What does Cassie find in the library?
a) A key
b) A strange book **1pt**
c) A cat

3 What do the bullies turn into? **2pts**

4 *Fill in the sentence:*
Fairies hate _____. It makes them feel sick. **3pts**

5 What is happening in the image below? **2pts**

6 *Multiple Choice:*
In the end, how do Tiff and Cassie get the Fairy Queen back in the book? **1pt**
a) Cassie sneaks up behind her
b) Tiff ties her up
c) Tiff casts a spell on her

Answers on the next page. Every correct answer earns points (pts) Which level are you?

Level:
0 - 1pts = Troll
2 - 4pts = Elf
5 - 7pts = Pixie
8 - 9pts = Witch
10pts = Fairy Queen

Join the Court Answers

1=(a), 2=(b), 3=Rats, 4=Iron, 5=Tiff is using her necklace to scare the Fairy Queen away, 6=(a)

Explore...

Think about the following:

- Why do you think Cassie isn't scared of the bullies anymore?

- What other creatures could be hiding in the magic book? What would happen if they got out?

- Do you think the bullies will leave Cassie alone now?

Other Titles

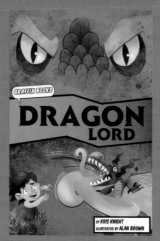